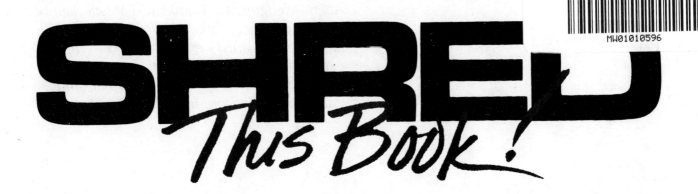

SHRED This Book!

THE *SCANDALOUS* CARTOONS OF DOUG *Marlette*

PEACHTREE PUBLISHERS, LTD.

Acknowledgments: Thanks to Paulette Lambert, for her patience, fathomless production skills, and unerring artist's eye; Chuck Perry for his exquisite editorial judgment; and Laura Mace and Larry Presslar for their usual flair and grace in helping produce the cover design.

Published by
Peachtree Publishers, Ltd.
494 Armour Circle, NE
Atlanta, Georgia 30324

Manufactured in the United States of America

10 9 8 7 6 5 4 3 2 1

Laura Mace, front cover design
Mark Sluder, cover photo
Paulette Lambert, book design

Library of Congress Catalog Card Number 88-60003

ISBN 0-934601-46-1

SHRED
This Book!

For Melinda and Jackson

Foreword

Paradox runs deep in my veins. My people were classically Southern — mill workers, cotton farmers, tobacco farmers, and all very poor. The South was hit hardest by the depression, long before it became fashionable in other parts of the country. Out of that economic deprivation came some of the most ardent New Dealers, people who realized that something drastic and radical had to be done. My grandfather was one of them. He voted for Franklin Roosevelt four times, ". . . and I'd vote for him again today if he was running," he once told me.

I asked why, and he explained, "Because he was the only president who cared anything about poor people."

I was impressed by my grandfather's shimmering populist sentiments, but then he added, "The only mistake he ever made was he should have let Hitler kill them Jews." That sort of gut-wrenching contradiction was not unusual in my family.

I learned recently that my grandmother was once bayoneted by a National Guardsman during a mill strike. And that my grandfather himself was president of a union. There are rebellious genes floating around inside of me, and that may help explain where my willingness to challenge authority and question power comes from.

...THE OLD-FASHIONED WAY.

Editorial cartoons, by their very nature, challenge conventional thought. You will never see a good cartoon that says, "Three cheers for the status quo!" or "Hooray for the way things are!" Cartoons are a vehicle of attack, so the best ones possess a certain fury. The best satirists — Jonathan Swift, Mark Twain, Joseph Heller, Walker Percy — are disappointed with the way things have turned out, and they express a basic rage in their work. The trick is to channel that rage in a constructive way. Satirists use their rage to clarify and illuminate values.

That's one of the things I like most about my work — confronting contradictions, pointing out the ironies and holding my own prism up to the light and looking at issues from my own perspective. I like showing the banality of evil. I like to show that goofy, mundane people sometimes do horrible things — punching a time clock at Auschwitz. I like turning symbols upside down and inside out and playing with images so that they are not so predictable. I enjoy taking familiar symbols and clichés which have been trivialized and denuded of meaning and retooling their content and restoring their meaning by looking at them with new eyes.

Every artist looks at things in a certain way — whether it is Cezanne seeing trees in his way or Picasso seeing human beings in his. Cartoonists also see things in their particular way. And there is no "correct" way, as long as we are effective, evocative, and say something worth saying. I trust that the work in this volume is all three.

"QUICK—GIMME A HUNDRED TWENTY BILLION QUARTERS!"

MARLETTE ©1987
THE ATLANTA CONSTITUTION

Me the People

10

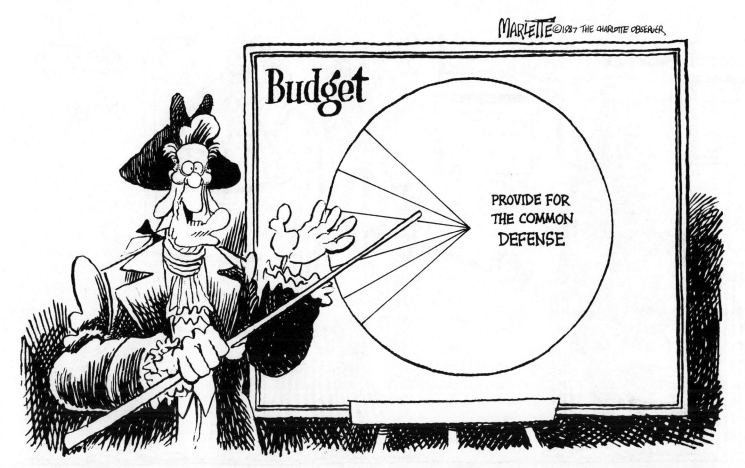

"...SO WE HAD TO CUT BACK ON FORMING A MORE PERFECT UNION, ESTABLISHING JUSTICE, PROMOTING THE GENERAL WELFARE, INSURING DOMESTIC TRANQUILITY, AND SECURING THE BLESSINGS OF LIBERTY FOR OURSELVES AND OUR POSTERITY!..."

"SORRY—I'VE DEPROGRAMMED MOONIES AND I'VE DEPROGRAMMED HARE KRISHNAS, BUT THERE'S NOTHING I CAN DO WITH 'YOUTH FOR REAGAN'!"

HAIL TO THE CHIEF

13

"GEE, GUYS, CAN'T THIS WAIT? I'M TALKING TO ED MEESE ABOUT THE IMPORTANCE OF PROTECTING THE UNBORN!"

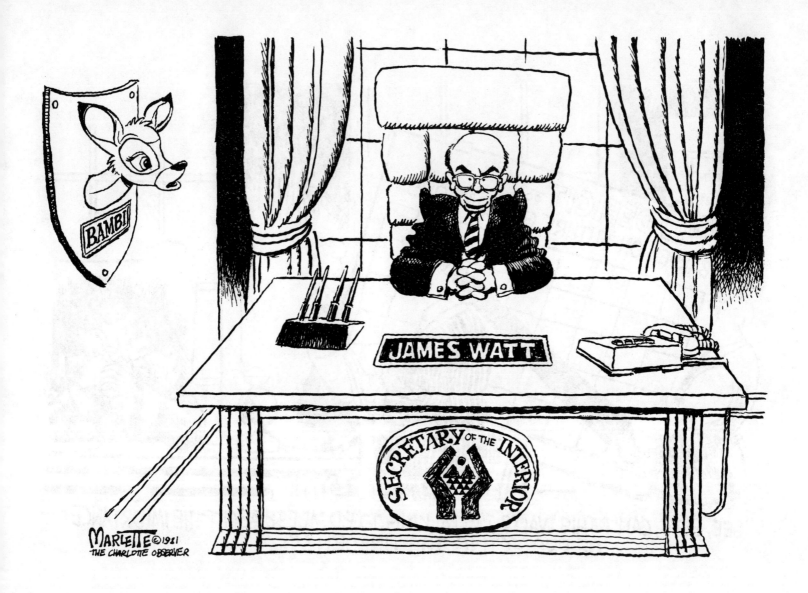

" HEY, **WIMP**!....WHATCHA GOT IN THE LUNCH PAIL?"

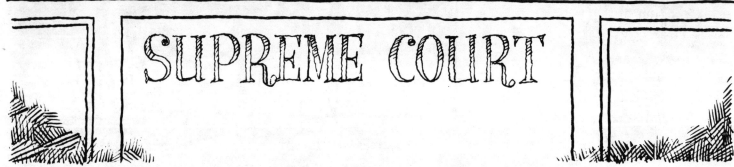

18

"I TOLD YOU THE SUPREME COURT DISAPPROVED OF THAT SORT OF THING!"

"YEAH, BORK WILL BE THE SWING VOTE!"

"GINSBURG HERE IS MY CHOICE FOR THE HIGH COURT!"

MARLETTE ©1987
THE ATLANTA CONSTITUTION

WHITE

COLORED

SUPREME COURT

MARLETTE ©1987
THE ATLANTA CONSTITUTION

23

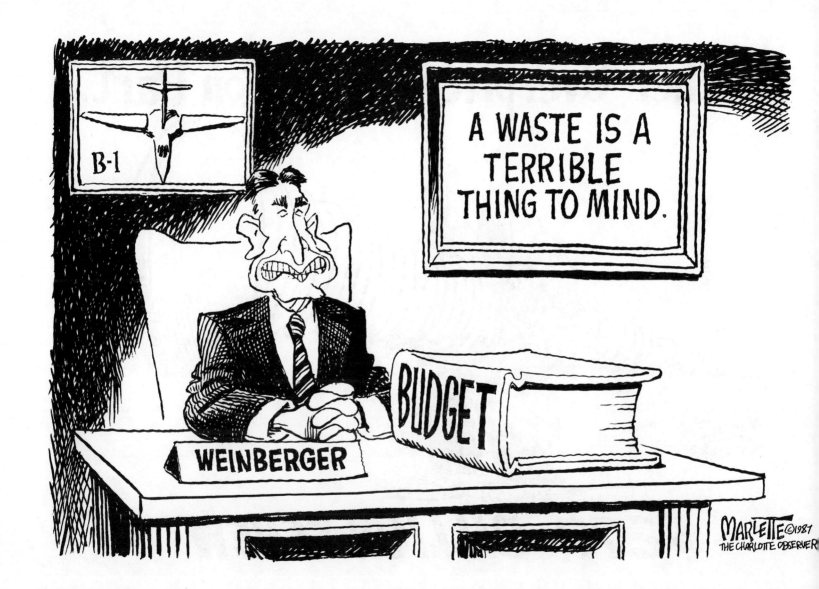

25

Another Overpriced Pentagon Part...

$277 BILLION SCREW

27

30

31

"IT'S FOOLPROOF, COMRADES — THEIR DEFENSES ARE HELPLESS AGAINST IT!...
WE SMUGGLE A WARHEAD INTO THE U.S. IN A SHIPMENT OF MARIJUANA!"

"THANK GOD HE'S NOT ON DRUGS OR STEROIDS — HE'S JUST A DRUNK!"

"MY PARENTS SAY IF THEY EVER CATCH ME DOING DRUGS THEY'LL KILL ME—
BUT I DON'T KNOW IF THAT'S THEM OR THE ALCOHOL TALKING!"

"WE HOLD THESE TRUTHS TO BE SELF-EVIDENT.... EXCEPT TO ED MEESE!"

" I SEE NO EVIDENCE OF HUNGRY CHILDREN IN AMERICA! "

"NO, MEESE—THE URINE SAMPLE GOES IN HERE!"

"THIS IS ATTORNEY GENERAL ED MEESE!... I KNOW I'M IN HERE!... I'VE GOT ME SURROUNDED!... IF I DON'T COME OUT WITH MY HANDS UP I'M COMING IN AFTER ME!"

"PATIENCE—WHEN MEESE GETS HERE WE'LL HAVE A QUORUM!"

39

"FAWN! HOW DO YOU TURN THIS SUCKER OFF?!"

"COLONEL NORTH COULDN'T MAKE IT TO THE HEARINGS TODAY, BUT HE SENT ALONG HIS UNIFORM FOR QUESTIONING!"

"YOU HAVE THE RIGHT TO REMAIN SILENT!... YOU HAVE THE RIGHT TO AN ATTORNEY GENERAL!..."

Render Unto Caesar

Although my cartoons have sometimes been labeled the work of a card-carrying secular humanist, I believe I learned much about my craft in Sunday School. The parables of Jesus, in a way, were like cartoons: illustrations with a point.

Most of the values in my drawings can be traced to civics classes in junior high and Sunday School classes at Magnolia Street Baptist Church in Laurel, Mississippi. As any Southern Baptist can tell you, Baptists spend a lot of time in church — Sunday School, morning worship, Training Union, Evening Worship, Wednesday Night Prayer Meeting, Sunbeams, Royal Ambassadors, on and on. And, in case none of that took, there were the perennial revival meetings.

I remember one such revival vividly and what probably was a pivotal moment for me as a budding satirist. During the hellfire and brimstone sermon, I listened attentively to the preacher fulminating against sin. He punctuated every point with the pronouncement that, "The world is in chaos," pronouncing it each time with feeling, "ko-ahs!" Although I was then only twelve years old, I was sufficiently familiar with the English language to know that the word was pronounced "kay-ahs". I recall cringing in embarrassment for the preacher. To my mind, his authority had been sabotaged. Perhaps this marked my first glimmer of recognition that authorities, religious as well as secular, were to be questioned. A cartoonist was born.

FUNDAMENTALIST BOOK OF THE MONTH CLUB

MARLETTE ©1981
THE CHARLOTTE OBSERVER

BIBLICAL INERRANCY TEST ➡

DO YOU BELIEVE THIS CHURCH DOCTRINE IS **LITERALLY TRUE?**

IF SO, YOU MAY QUALIFY AS A BIBLE-BELIEVIN', BORN-AGAIN, FUNDAMENTALIST **SOUTHERN BAPTIST!**

" HE BURNED HIS BIBLE BY MISTAKE ! "

"WE SUGGEST PRAYER!"

"HOT DANG, EDNA—I GOT ME A SECULAR HUMANIST!"

"UH-OH!...THE SECULAR HUMANISTS ARE BACK!"

"NOW WE JUST THROW THE MODERATES TO THE FUNDAMENTALISTS!"

"JOHN, THE SOUTHERN BAPTIST!"

"WE'LL TAKE ANYTHING WITH A WARNING LABEL!"

MARLETTE ©1986
THE CHARLOTTE OBSERVER

"SOMETHING'S GOTTA BE DONE ABOUT ILLITERACY IN THIS COUNTRY—
THE KIDS CAN'T READ THE TV LISTINGS ANYMORE!"

In Mammon We Trust

KEYS TO THE KINGDOM

I was poking fun at PTL before poking fun at PTL was cool. The bizarre antics of Jim and Tammy Bakker and their Charlotte-based religious Disney World was doggedly covered by *The Charlotte Observer* before the national media joined in. As *The Observer's* editorial cartoonist I was truly blessed. This whacky televangelism soap-opera provided endless cartoon fodder.

One of my first cartoons on PTL was drawn back in 1978 when Jim Bakker, due to his legendary financial mismanagement, abruptly and unceremoniously canned a significant portion of his staff. The day the cartoon appeared a reporter returned from PTL headquarters where he was told that Jim was very upset by the cartoon — a drawing of Bakker sitting at the center of Da Vinci's famous Last Supper intoning to the disciples: "I don't quite know how to break this to you, but I'm afraid I'm going to have to let some of you go!"

Bakker aides claimed that, in fact, Jim was on his knees weeping into the carpet over the cartoon. I pointed out that a weeping Jim Bakker was hardly an indication of serious emotional trauma. If you

watched the show you knew he and Tammy could wax hysterical over anything — from lost souls to burnt toast, from the breakdown in traditional values to going off daylight savings time.

" SORRY, THERE'S NO ROOM—WE'RE FULL OF TELEVANGELISTS!"

In those early days when PTL was only a local story, before it had burned itself into the national and international consciousness, any cartoon on PTL would provoke strong negative reaction from PTL followers. They protested with phone calls, letters and threats. As the tension between Bakker and *The Charlotte Observer* grew over the years, Bakker would attack the paper virulently on the air, holding up the cartoons on camera, urging viewers to cancel subscriptions, phone in and mail in complaints, and otherwise harass us. They would characterize the newspaper and its cartoonist as "tools of Satan." I assured callers who echoed that charge that it was impossible that I might be a tool of Satan because our personnel department gave tests that screened for

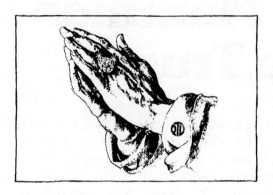

that sort of thing. Knight-Ridder newspapers had a policy, I explained, against hiring tools of Satan.

In 1987, when Jim confessed to messing around with a church secretary and resigned, the whole lurid tale of Pearlygate unfolded in all its seamy detail, a kind of emotional pornography. A mesmerized nation learned what we in Charlotte had been documenting for more than a decade — the waterslides, crystal palaces, Tammy Faye's shopping demons, the malfeasance and mismanagement, the carnival of tacky excess that was PTL.

When Bakker resigned and was replaced by Jerry Falwell, I drew a cartoon of Falwell as a snake in the PTL paradise saying, "Jim and Tammy were driven from the garden but they left me in charge!" At the time Falwell was being hailed as a hero in the media, arriving to rescue the ministry of his fallen brethren. That particular

cartoon drove the beleaguered PTL'ers even more bananas. According to *Newsweek,* the PTL replacement TV host, long-time Bakker friend and now-defrocked minister Richard Dortch, "put the blame on *The Charlotte Observer,* brandishing a cartoon that showed Falwell as a snake in the Garden of Eden. The real target, he warned 'is not Jim and Tammy Bakker, it isn't Richard Dortch, it isn't Jerry Falwell. It's God's work.' The audience wept and sang."

Falwell and his minions complained loudly to editors and reporters about that cartoon, demanding apologies. I explained to angry callers and worried editors that there is ample precedent in the New Testament for referring to religious professionals as snakes. Jesus called the pharisees, the spokesmen for the "moral majority" of their time, a "brood of vipers." John the Baptist was less genteel. I know, because I learned something about drawing cartoons in Sunday School.

MARLETTE ©1985 THE CHARLOTTE OBSERVER

AMERICAN EXCESS

JIM BAKKER

PTL

" HI !... DO YOU KNOW ME ?... "

"BLESSED ARE THE T.V. EVANGELISTS— FOR THEY SHALL INHERIT THE GOLD COAST CONDO!"

59

"THAT'S RIGHT—JIM AND TAMMY WERE EXPELLED FROM PARADISE AND LEFT ME IN CHARGE!"

HE IS RISEN

MARLETTE ©1987
THE ATLANTA CONSTITUTION

"RELAX—IT'S JUST JIM AND TAMMY COMING AGAIN!"

MARLETTE ©1987
THE CHARLOTTE OBSERVER

From Sea To Shining Sea

"GIMME A SATURDAY NIGHT SPECIAL, A BUCKET OF AMMO, AND AN ORDER OF CONGRESSMEN ON THE SIDE!"

"I TOLD YOU FLORIDA NEVER SHOULD HAVE RELAXED ITS GUN LAWS!..."

"NO, IT'S NOT A MELTDOWN—THEY JUST FOUND OUT ABOUT THE RATE INCREASE!"

GROSS NUCLEAR MUTATIONS

Fig. A

Fig. B

"REMEMBER WHEN THEY USED TO SEND US POVERTY PROGRAMS!..."

"WHY, WHEN I WAS A BOY WE WERE SO BAD OFF WE DIDN'T HAVE A SINGLE CELEBRITY INTERESTED IN OUR PLIGHT!"

"DON'T BLAME ME—YOU'RE THE ONE WHO INSISTED ON A FROZEN EMBRYO!..."

"....THEN THE BOTTOM DROPPED OUTA OIL....I HAD TO SELL THE HOUSE WITH THE CEMENT POND; ELLIE MAE DRIFTED INTO SKIN FLICKS; JETHRO'S DEALIN' DRUGS, AND GRANNY'S A BAG LADY ON WILSHIRE BOULEVARD!"

" TAKE TWO ASPIRIN AND SUE ME IN THE MORNING!"

"AS, LIKE, CLASS VALEDICTORIAN, YOU KNOW, I WAS TRYING TO THINK, YOU KNOW, IN MY HEAD, LIKE, WHAT TO SAY AND JUNK.....AND, YOU KNOW, LIKE IT'S REALLY WEIRD BUT TWELVE YEARS OF PUBLIC EDUCATION — I MEAN, WHOA!.....ANYWAY, THAT'S WHAT I THINK IN MY HEAD, YOU KNOW?"

"NO, I DON'T WANT TO KNOW WHAT BILL COSBY WOULD DO IN A CASE LIKE THIS!"

FIRST DOLLAR

FIRST 59¢

82

"I'M GONNA PASS THE TOYOTA, HONEY— COVER ME!"

" IT'S BEEN ONE OF THOSE WEEKS!"

MARLETTE ©1986
THE CHARLOTTE OBSERVER

86

Challenger

I heard about the Challenger shuttle disaster on my car radio almost immediately after the explosion. A couple of hours later, as I sat down at my drawing board to come up with an appropriate image, my editor notified me that the Observer was putting out a special edition on the disaster that afternoon. If I wanted a drawing in that edition I would have to have it completed in 45 minutes. I quickly settled on a simple image of an American eagle gazing into the heavens with a single tear falling from its eye.

The drawing hit the streets that afternoon in our special edition and ran again the following morning. I arrived at work the next day to find a bouquet of flowers, sent by readers, in front of my office door. People called in weeping. Requests for reprints overwhelmed *The Observer.* Five hundred large reproductions were printed, and an italic notice ran at the bottom of the editorial page notifying readers of their availability. They were all snapped up by ten o'clock the same morning the notice appeared. Another thousand were printed and they were gone by two o'clock that day. Yet another thousand were gone by four. People were driving all the way downtown to *The Observer* lobby to pick them up. The reprints were then made available by mail as well. An *Observer* story on the response later reported, "Grandmothers wanted copies for heirlooms. People planned to frame it. High Schools included it in yearbooks. 'Looked like they were giving away Cadillacs,' said Monnie Heafner at the lobby console . . . 'It was a madhouse,' said Denise Stowe in the Customer Service Shop. *Observer* presses began multiple runs. 'I would bring them up from the print shop and people would attack the dolly,' said Jessie Ozmelek in the Marketing Services Division. . . ."

There were letters to the editor and hundreds of letters and notes of appreciation that poured in along with reader mail-orders:

"Deep in my heart, when I heard the news of the explosion I felt a sorrow I could not express. Then Marlette . . . expressed it for me and I cried, and cried, and cried."

"Your shuttle cartoon prints will definitely be a part of the heritage gifts I have planned for my children and grandchildren."

"Please send me one copy of Doug Marlette's cartoon. This improved my impression of him by 100 percent."

To date *The Charlotte Observer* has distributed more than 60,000 prints of the drawing. Copies went out all over the country. They went to the astronauts' families. They were sent to NASA headquarters. They hang in homes, offices and restaurants thoughout the Carolinas. Requests come in to reprint the image on tee-shirts, wall hangings, even RV spare tire covers. Musicians even wrote songs inspired by the image. I still receive requests for copies two years after the tragic event that inspired the drawing.

What is behind such an outpouring of emotion? Certainly the collective witness of a nation to such a mythic, watershed event is part of it.

Perhaps it's also the simplicity, wordless and direct, of the image — the archaic expression of unexpressible sorrow.

I sometimes characterize the cartoonist's role as that of the newspaper's designated feeler. Unlike our objective, emotionally distant, journalistic colleagues, cartoonists are emotional teabags. We're the ones with the epidermis of semi-permeable membrane, the ones who allow events to get through our defenses and under our skin. At our best, like any artist, we should respond with passion and feeling, simplicity and directness. With some skill and luck, as perhaps with the Shuttle cartoon, we may hit on something. We may occasionally get in touch with that which is basic and common to us all, that which can move us so deeply — the primitive power of pictures. The stuff of dreams.

NASA's New Improved O-Ring

MARLETTE ©1986
THE CHARLOTTE OBSERVER

...THAT'S RIGHT, DAN...PERHAPS THE MOST AMAZING PIECE OF DEBRIS RECOVERED FROM THE SPACE SHUTTLE IS THIS:

PRESIDENT REAGAN'S NAIVETE...

...HIS TOUCHING FAITH IN SOPHISTICATED SPACE TECHNOLOGY...

MARLETTE ©1986
THE CHARLOTTE OBSERVER

...THE PRESIDENT'S BELIEF THAT MILLIONS OF COMPU-TERIZED GADGETS WILL FUNCTION FLAWLESSLY WITH HAIR-TRIGGER TIMING TO PROTECT US FROM MISSILE ATTACK...

...BY ALL RIGHTS, THIS SHOULD HAVE BEEN VAPO-RIZED IN THE EXPLOSION LIKE MOST EVERYTHING ELSE...

...YET HERE IT IS STILL INTACT. INCREDIBLE! BACK TO YOU, DAN.

91

Us vs. Them

"I ONLY REGRET THAT YOU HAVE BUT ONE LIFE TO GIVE FOR MY CONTRAS!"

MORAL EQUIVALENT OF FOUNDING FATHERS

MORAL EQUIVALENT OF BUNKER HILL

MORAL EQUIVALENT OF REDCOATS

MORAL EQUIVALENT OF A PRESIDENT

IF YOU LIKED THE TEE SHIRT...

...YOU'LL WANT THE ENTIRE LINE OF "CONTRA-AID" PRODUCTS!.....

HONK IF YOU LOVE QUAGMIRES!

NICARAGUA I FOUND IT!

BUMPER STICKERS

I ♥ VIETNAMS

MUGS

SELECTIVE SERVICE SYSTEM
Greetings:

GREETING CARDS

U.S. ARMY

MARLETTE ©1986 THE CHARLOTTE OBSERVER

TOTE BAGS

ACCESSORIES

"MAKE-UP! LET'S TRY ANOTHER POWDERED WIG — WE'RE HAVING TROUBLE PASSING HIM OFF AS A FOUNDING FATHER!"

♪ MY CONTRAS, 'TIS OF THEE... ♪

♪ ...DEALING DRUGS AND MISERY... ♪

♪ ...OF THEE I SING!... ♪

HOLD BACK THE COMMIE TIDE...
WE'LL PAY YOU FOR THE RIDE... ♪

...THAT'S WHY MY HERO OLLIE LIED... ♪

...VIETNAMIZING! ♪

MARLETTE ©1988
THE ATLANTA CONSTITUTION

"THIS NEW TECHNOLOGY PREVENTS WAR BY KNOCKING OUT THE ENEMY'S WEAPONS FROM THE HEAVENS—WE CALL IT 'STAR WARS'!"

"IN THE HEROIC STRUGGLE AGAINST IMPERIALIST AGGRESSION, OUR GLORIOUS SOVIET RADIOACTIVITY WAS INVITED ACROSS NEIGHBORING EUROPEAN BORDERS TODAY...."

MARLETTE ©1987
THE ATLANTA CONSTITUTION

"... AND FILLING IN FOR JOHNNY THIS WEEK IS *MIKHAIL GORBACHEV!...*"

"GORBACHEV'S GONE TOO FAR!"

MARLETTE ©1985
THE CHARLOTTE OBSERVER

"YOU HEARD ME — COLOREDS TO THE BACK OF THE BUS!"

" REMEMBER—NO MATTER HOW IT LOOKS, I'M ON YOUR SIDE! "

107

"YOUR CHILD WAS KILLED AT MY CHILD'S FUNERAL?... I THOUGHT MY CHILD WAS KILLED AT YOUR CHILD'S FUNERAL!"

JERRY FALWELL'S Worst Nightmare:

LITTLE BLACK RAMBO

" GIVE ME YOUR RICH, YOUR FAMOUS, YOUR NOBEL LAUREATES, YOUR RUSSIAN POETS AND POLISH EMISSARIES, YOUR RESPECTABLE WHITE ANTI-SOVIETS YEARNING TO BREATHE FREE...... "

"...WE'RE ALL OUT OF BREAD AND SUGAR... OH, AND WE'RE RUNNING LOW ON ANTI-TANK WEAPONS — SO DON'T FORGET TO PICK UP SOME HOSTAGES!"

"WE STARTED OUT REFLAGGING KUWAITI TANKERS!..."

MARLETTE ©1986
THE CHARLOTTE OBSERVER

118

"IT'S OUR SPECIAL BOMB FOR LIBYA— IT TAKES OUT MILITARY BASES, HOMES, EMBASSIES AND CIVILIANS, BUT LEAVES U.S. OIL COMPANIES STANDING !.."

OCCUPIED WEST BANK

"ANNE FRANK!"

Helms in a Handbasket

Jesse Helms used to ask me for the original drawings of my cartoons. When I was a young, inexperienced cartoonist, I would sometimes send them to him and he would hang them on the wall of his office in the U.S. Senate. They were not flattering cartoons. But, for a politician, I suppose, as long as you spell the name right . . . I used to get a kick out of the idea that these subversive doodles were wallpapering the office of the senior senator from Right Field.

MARLETTE ©1985
THE CHARLOTTE OBSERVER

HOW ABOUT A MANDATORY MOMENT OF SILENCE FOR U.S. SENATORS?

123

♪ ♫ CAROLINA MOON KEEPS SHINING.... ♫ ♪

Somewhere over the years, though, Helms stopped asking for the originals and began complaining to my publisher. (Democrats, I have noticed, complain to the cartoonist. Republicans go straight to the publisher.)

I'm not sure when the drawings started getting under the skin of Senator Helms. It may have been when I drew him and his colleague, Senator John East, as Tweedledum and Tweedledummer. Or maybe it was during Helms' scurrilous assault on the Martin Luther King Holiday and I suggested a national holiday honoring Senator Helms: April Fool's Day. Or perhaps it was when the Tarheel State led the nation in turkey production and I drew a flock of turkeys and included Senator Helms among them.

But the cartoon that generated the most negative reponse of any I have ever done was one drawn right after Helms won the notoriously nasty U.S. Senate race of 1984 against Gov. Jim Hunt. Helms was depicted with trousers dropped, smiling out at the reader, mooning the Capitol building. The caption read: Carolina Moon Keeps Shining.

Helms' office stopped returning phone calls to our Washington reporter and refused to talk to *The Charlotte Observer* until he got, in his words, "an official apology from the publisher." I don't know if he ever got one but, of course, the Senator resumed speaking to our reporters as soon as he had something he wanted to appear in the paper.

126

TWEEDLEDUM AND TWEEDLEDUMMER

"IF I TOLD JESSE HELMS ONCE, I TOLD HIM A THOUSAND TIMES:
'DON'T LEAVE HOME WITHOUT IT!'"

Wannabees '88

129

OLD SOLDIERS NEVER DIE, THEY JUST FADE AWAY

131

"JEEPERS! I LOVE IT!"

134

Front Runner

Gary, Gary, quite contrary...

MARLETTE ©1988
THE ATLANTA CONSTITUTION

How does your campaign grow?

With ideas new, and matching funds, too...

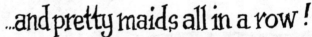

...and pretty maids all in a row!

"THE WHITE HOUSE? YOU CAN'T GET THERE FROM HERE!"

"PRESIDENT?... NO, CHILD, BUT YOU CAN GROW UP TO BE FRONT-RUNNER!"

" I WAS BORN AND RAISED IN THE BRIAR PATCH! "

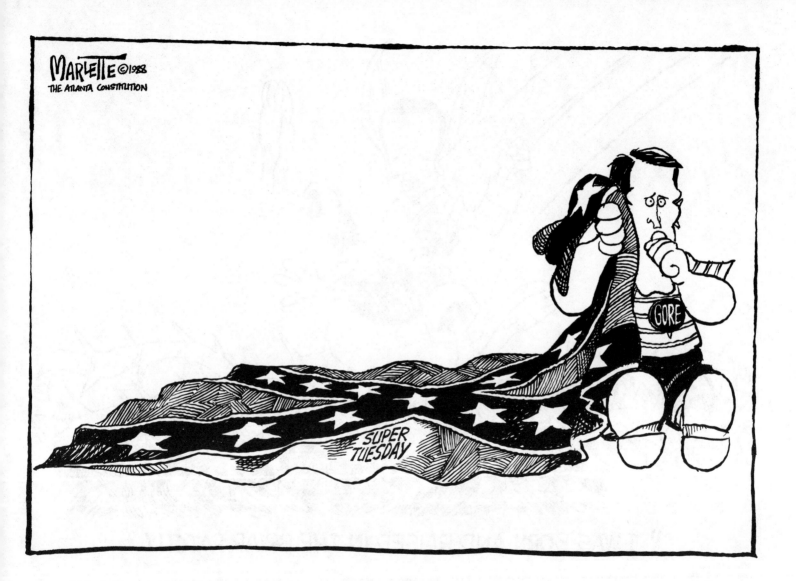

142

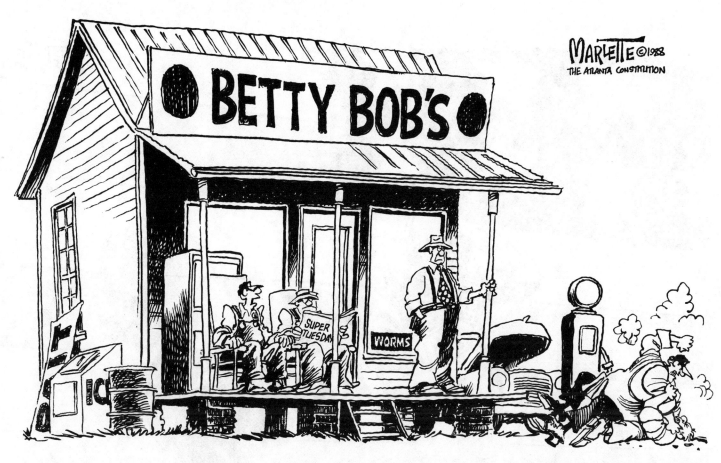

"BUBBA SAID GEPHARDT'S THIRTY SECOND SPOTS HAD SLICKER PRODUCTION VALUES THAN GORE'S THIRTY SECOND SPOTS!"

Afterword

Cartoonists receive lots of mail — suggestions for cartoons, requests for drawings, occasional fan mail and, if they are doing their job, hate mail. I have grown accustomed to receiving envelopes covered with lots of American flag decals, scriptural passages scrawled across the margins and addresses with every other letter printed in red, white and blue magic marker. These are the unmistakable trappings of hate mail. Usually the envelope is soiled, the handwriting an illegible scrawl. If the letter is typed, it's typed in all upper case with lots of underlining for emphasis. Often the offending drawing is simply torn out and something unpleasant is scribbled across it. Or

" SORRY—WE ONLY RESCUE FETUSES !"

some label or caption is changed, usually reworded to cast aspersions upon my forebears. Sometimes the critique is written on a roll of toilet paper. A recent missive which now hangs on my bulletin board suggests that I "don't have brians to think with." That's right, "brians."

I was introduced to hate mail early in my professional career. I was 22 years old and had just been hired by *The Charlotte Observer* when a cartoon I drew supporting amnesty for draft resisters set off a barrage of irate letters to the editor. They included a petition signed by 35 residents of surrounding communities urging that I be canned. This ignited a reaction from readers supporting the cartoon, who gathered a petition to keep the cartoonist. The debate was on.

Marlette editorial cartoons caused such a disturbance during that first turbulent year of my professional career that John S. Knight, owner of the Knight newspaper chain, and his brother Jim Knight, then absentee publisher of *The Charlotte Observer,* put pressure on *Observer* Editor C.A. (Pete) McKnight and Executive Editor Jim Batten (now president of Knight-Ridder newspapers) to get rid of me. To the *Observer's* credit, its editors defended their right to run outrageous cartoons in its pages. Less admirably, they banished the

Marlette cartoons to the op-ed page. As Jules Feiffer has pointed out, op-ed pages are a "free press way of apologizing for the first amendment."

But volatile reaction to drawings is not just limited to letter writers or overly sensitive publishers. At one point, early in the Reagan years, a group of prominent businessmen visited my editor urging that I be fired because, as they explained, the nation was, with the election of Reagan, at a critical juncture and the Marlette cartoons criticizing the president were "a threat to civilization." Over the years, the cartoons have garnered complaints from across the spectrum of opinion, depending on whose sacred cow was poked that day — from Republican businessmen defending their president, to liberal activists dissatisfied with a cartoon's degree of ideological purity, from white supremacists regularly calling me a "nigger-lover" to some of Atlanta's black establishment claiming drawings lampooning Julian Bond's drug and marital problems were racist.

A few years ago, local officials from Jewish groups complained to editors that cartoons critical of Begin's invasion of Lebanon were anti-Semitic. They complained that I drew Begin with a big

LAND OF THE FREE, HOME OF THE BRAVE

nose and compared my cartoons to the ugly anti-Semitic Nazi propaganda cartoons of the Thirties. I explained that I drew Begin's nose big because it was, in fact, big. I suggested that these critics focused on the size of Begin's nose because it was easier to defend his nose than his policies. My editors took the strategic position that I drew everyone's nose big. That discussion, held in an editor's office with the offended groups, I am told, degenerated to the point where editorial pages were spread on the floor measuring and comparing with a ruler the noses of various Jewish and non-Jewish figures in my cartoons. Something about the nature of cartoons seems to bring out this kind of behavior in otherwise rational human beings.

Good cartoonists should expect hate mail. After all, if you express opinions in a strong and provocative manner you must expect there will be others who disagree and will express their views likewise.

Personally, I find it bracing. Reader reaction, whether positive or negative, I consider healthy. It's an indication that the drawing was effective and that the reader or letter writer had a pulse.

The free expression of ideas and opinion is the lifeblood of a free society. Notice what happens when there is a revolution or *coup d'etat* in any country. Whether it is a revolution of the Right or Left, the first thing to go is the free press. Dictators understand the fundamental role of commerce and politics, that information is power. If you control the information, you've got the upper hand. The stunning wisdom of our founding fathers was that they placed that power — the right to information, to know what's going on — in the hands of the people. That's how we got and how we keep government of, for, and by the people.

The best cartoonists play the role of point man for the first amendment — the ones out front, on the perimeter, who catch the flak first. They are the mine-sweeps testing the boundaries and claiming new ground for free expression. With skill and luck they avoid being blown away by society's most repressive impulses.

"Are you censored?" I am often asked. Seldom, if ever. Newspapers hire cartoonists whose work they feel comfortable with and cartoonists try to join newspapers whose policies they are reasonably in tune with. I have seldom had disagreements with editors over the opinion expressed by the cartoon or had a cartoon killed outright because an editor disagreed with a point the cartoon was making. The differences, when they arose, have had more to do with the fundamental difference between a drawing and an editorial.

Cartoons are "visual rock and roll." Like the "jungle music" of Elvis and Little Richard, as it was called by parents uneasy about rock's implications for the young, a good cartoon is "jungle art" — it's primitive and dangerous. It gets to you, like rock music. It gets under people's skin. It's popular, it's people's art. Pictures come before words. In the history of the human species, words and language arrive much later than images. We are all born dreamers and are fluent in the archaic language of images.

And if cartoons are like rock and roll jungle music, editors tend to be like the parents of the Fifties — harrumphing, raising eyebrows and vaguely uneasy with rock and roll art's implications for society and the young. Because editors are word people, they are more comfortable with words and the civilization that language brings. Often they are control freaks. The restriction and restraint that civilization entails feels better to them than the wild untamed passion, energy and humor of jungle art.

Of course, the best editors recognize that good cartoons shade more towards art than journalism. The fundamentals of journalism are fairness, even-handedness, objectivity. The fundamentals of cartooning are distortion, hyperbole, subjectivity. Cartoons are not just about facts, they are about meaning — their distortion gets at the essence, the truth that is greater than the sum of the facts. Cartoons distort and reflect reality like fun-house mirrors, and if we are not too insistent upon literal representation and doctrinal purity, we can sometimes catch in them a glimpse of some hidden truth about ourselves.

158